101 PANCHATANTRA STORIES

D1501158

DREAMLAND PUBLICATIONS

J-128, Kirti Nagar, New Delhi-110 015, India

Tel. : +91-11-2510 6050, 2543 5657

E-mail : dreamland@dreamlandpublications.com

Shop online at www.dreamlandpublications.com

Follow us on www.instagram.com/dreamland.publications

Published in 2022 by
DREAMLAND PUBLICATIONS
J-128, Kirti Nagar, New Delhi - 110 015, India
Tel : +91-11-2510 6050, 2543 5657
E-mail : dreamland@dreamlandpublications.com, www.dreamlandpublications.com
Copyright © 2022 Dreamland Publications
All rights reserved. No part of this publication should be reproduced, stored in a retrieval system or transmitted in any form or by any means—electronic, mechanical, photocopying, recording or otherwise—without the prior permission of Dreamland Publications.
Printed in India

Contents

1. THE MONKEY AND THE CROCODILE

Once a crocodile took some jambolan fruit for his wife, given by his friend monkey. But his wife was not happy. "I want to eat the monkey's heart!" she said. Though sad the crocodile decided to get the monkey's heart for his wife. The next day, when the crocodile visited the monkey, he said, "My wife has asked me to call you for dinner." The monkey happily jumped on the crocodile's back. But as soon as he jumped, the crocodile told him about his wife, who wanted his heart. "Oh, my dear friend. Why did you not tell me before? I left my heart on the tree. Let's swim back and get it," said the monkey. The crocodile took the monkey back. As soon as they reached the tree, the monkey jumped and went to the highest branch. "You fool! How can anyone live without a heart?" the monkey said while throwing fruits at the crocodile.

Moral: Foolishness can make you take wrong decisions.

2. THE FOOLISH DONKEY

One day, a farmer let the donkey loose at night, so that he could graze the fields. As the donkey was eating, he befriended a fox. The fox said, "Let us go to that maize field and enjoy more food." The donkey agreed. As they were grazing, the donkey turned to the fox and said, "I feel like singing."

"Are you foolish? You will wake the farmers of this field," the fox said in his hush voice. The donkey did not listen to the fox. Just as he was about to begin, the fox left him and went to hide behind the nearby bushes. With the loud braying of the donkey, the farmers of the maize field came running. They spotted the donkey and beat him up blue.

Moral: We must know the proper place and time for doing the things we want.

3. THE FOX AND THE GRAPES

On a bright sunny day, a fox spotted a vineyard. The vineyard was full of ripe, purple, big round grapes hanging on the creeper plant that hung high on a tree. The fox got hungry just by looking at these grapes. "These are so big, purple, and juicy. I'm sure they must be really sweet to eat," he thought to himself. The fox jumped to catch a bunch of grapes but failed. He tried again, but he could not reach them. He ran back and forth to build up speed so that he could jump high, but he failed again.

At last, he gave up after getting annoyed. "Well, I think these grapes aren't that sweet and ripe. I should go. I am just wasting my time." Saying this, he walked away.

Moral: If we give up easily, we will never know the goodness of things.

4. THE FARMER'S WIFE AND THE MONGOOSE

One beautiful day, a woman left her pet mongoose to care for her child while she went to the market. She told the mongoose to take care of the baby. But while she was gone, a snake came into the house. The mongoose killed the snake, who was about to bite the baby. When the mother came home, she saw blood in the mongoose's mouth. She thought it had hurt the baby. So she drove him away. But when she saw that the baby was fine, and a dead snake was lying nearby, she felt sad. "How foolish was I? I judged the pet too quickly," she cried. But it was of no use now.

Moral: We must not judge anyone quickly.

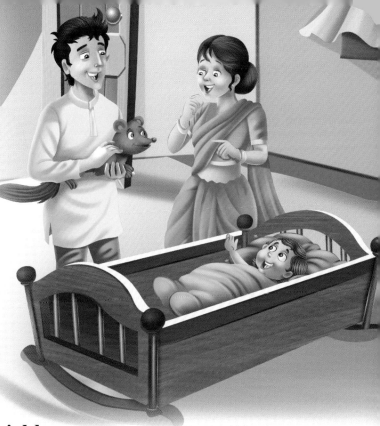

5. THE WEDDING OF THE MOUSE

A saint was praying by the river. As he was praying, an eagle came by and dropped a mouse on his lap. The saint believed the mouse to be unique as it came to him. So he prayed and changed the mouse into a pretty little girl. "Look, my dear wife, I have brought home this little one. From today, she'll be our daughter," he said. The saint and his wife took care of the little child. When she grew up to the age of getting married, her parents started searching for the right groom for her. The saint took her to the Sun God. "Father, he is too bright and hot. I can't marry him," she said, with her hands covering her face from the bright light of the Sun God. Then the saint took her to the Lord of Clouds. "But father, his thunder and darkness scare me," she said, shivering as she spoke to the saint. Just then, a mouse ran past them. "Oh father, the mouse is perfect. I shall marry him," she said, with eyes sparkling with joy. The saint was delighted to see his daughter happy.

Moral: We must choose what makes us happy.

6. THE FAR SIGHTED SWAN

Once there lived a group of swans on a tree. One day, they got trapped into a net laid by a hunter. Only the wise swan did not get captured as he was careful. But he was disappointed to see his friends struggling for freedom. He thought of a plan and said, "Friends, pretend as if you are dead. This will make the hunter place you on the ground. When he places all of you on the ground, you all fly away at once.' All the swans followed the wise swan's advice. The next morning, when the hunter saw the swans lying lifeless in the net, he was shocked. He took them out of the net and laid them carefully on the ground. And as he placed all of them on the ground, they flew away. The hunter could do nothing but repent at seeing them flying away.

Moral: Those who plan ahead of time will always find a way out.

7. THE BEDBUG AND THE MOSQUITO

One day, a mosquito came flying in and saw a family of bedbugs. It went up to the father bedbug and asked, "Sir, can you please leave some space for me? I would love to taste the King's blood by biting him," the mosquito said. "Alright, but wait till he is fast asleep, or you might wake him up if he's not deep in sleep," the father bedbug warned him and made him promise. So at night, when the bugs were ready to bite the King again, the mosquito came flying in and bit the King hard. The King shouted in pain, rubbing his hand hard. Hearing the King's cries, the King's guards came running in. The mosquito flew away. The King's guards started to beat the bed hardly, to remove bugs. While the bedbugs received beating, the mosquito laughed loudly at them!

Moral: Do not trust strangers so easily.

8. THE EAGLE AND THE WOODCUTTER

A kind-hearted woodcutter once rescued an eagle from a trap. Sometime later, the woodcutter had climbed on a steep hill to cuts trees for wood. There he got stuck, and couldn't come down. He sat on a rock, waiting for any help to come. Suddenly the eagle he had rescued came flying down towards him. In another moment, the eagle flew away with his hat. The woodcutter became angry and started to chase the eagle. After some time of tracking, he found the way to get down the hill. "Oh, so this is why you took my hat. You wanted me to run behind you and find this way. Thank you so much, my friend," the woodcutter said to the eagle.

Moral: Kindness will always get great rewards.

9. THE ROOSTER AND THE WEATHERVANE

A weathervane was sitting on the roof of a farmhouse. It was high above all the animals. It also made no sound. Among the animals was a very proud rooster. "Do you know, even roosters can lay eggs, like hens," the rooster said. The weathervane knew the rooster was lying and challenged the rooster to bring eggs. He asked the hens to check if the rooster was telling the truth. This way, everyone found out the rooster was lying. The rooster was very ashamed.

Moral: The person who lies will get in trouble one day.

10. THE DAYDREAMER

Once a lazy man hung his pot of milk above his head and started to dream about it. "With this pot of milk, I shall make some curd. Then I'll sell that curd, and buy more curd. Then I'll churn the curd and make butter. Then I will sell that butter and make lots of money. With that money, I will buy elephants. I will then sell the elephants and buy lots of gold and jewellery. I will marry a wealthy merchant's daughter. Then we will have a son. But what if my son is very naughty? What if he doesn't listen to me?. But in doing so, he kicked the pot of milk above his head. All the milk fell over him. The man woke up, only to realise it was his dream, and now he had no milk.

Moral: Don't dream of something that you are lazy to do in real life.

11. THE LAKE OF THE MOON

A herd of elephants attacked a forest of rabbits. The rabbit leader went to the Elephant king and said, "O king of elephants, I am a messenger of the moon. I have come here to tell you that the Almighty Moon is upset with you."

"What do you mean the Almighty Moon is upset with me?" asked the elephant king in fear.

"Well, this lake belongs to the Almighty Moon. Your herd has spoiled the whole lake. He is thinking of punishing you. So before he does something bad to you, run away!" the rabbit said, pointing his finger towards the forest exit. In fear, the elephant took his herd and ran away.

Moral: Wise thinking can save you from many things.

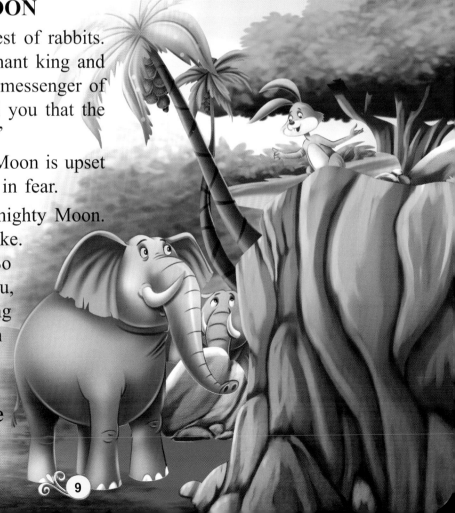

12. A THIEF'S SACRIFICE

Three friends, a young prince, a minister's son, and a merchant's son, decided to find some magic gems. So they set out to find those stones. As they searched the hill, they found three precious gems that were worth a lot of money. "We cannot be careless with them. How do we protect them?" the second friend asked. "Let's swallow them. This way, no one will know about these gems," the merchant's son said. So they did that. A thief had been observing them for quite some time. He liked their friendship and decided to join them. In doing so, he became their friend too. One day, they were travelling back to their village and decided to stop by at a chief's inn. The chief somehow found out about the gems. He was planning to capture them. But the thief found out and gave himself in place of his friends. The thief got imprisoned for life, while his friends escaped for their survival. The three young men were thankful to the thief who sacrificed himself and saved their lives.

Moral: A good deed will always be acknowledged.

13. STRENGTH IN UNITY

Once, a flock of parrots got caught in a bird catcher's net. The birds were in a panic. They tried to free themselves, but couldn't do so. One of the birds then calmed herself and turned towards her friends, saying, "Friends, let's not panic. On the count of three, we will fly together and take this net with us. That is how we will escape this trap." So all the parrots flapped their wings together and flew. The birdcatcher was in shock seeing the parrots wisdom and unity.

Moral: If you are working in unity, you can do anything.

14. THE SNAKE'S WIFE

A poor woodcutter and his wife had a snake for a child. Soon, the parents started to search for a bride for the snake. Finally, a friend agreed to marry the snake. One night, when the snake and his wife were sleeping, some magical lights appeared around the snake. The snake had turned into a handsome young man! Disturbed by the lights, the snake's wife woke up. She was in shock and was about to run. "Dear, it's me, your husband," the man said. "What? How is that possible? My husband is a snake," she said in tears. "I was the snake. But now my curse has lifted. Look, there lies my snakeskin," he said. The woman was happy, and so were the snake's parents.

Moral: Never lose hope, for miracles can happen anytime.

15. THE TRUE FRIENDS

There were four best friends – a mouse, a tortoise, a deer, and a crow. One day, their friend deer got caught in a hunter's trap. "Don't worry my friend, I will set you free," the mouse said while he nibbled the net to break it. The deer was free. But with all the noise, the hunter noticed them and came running. The deer, the mouse, and the crow escaped, but the slow tortoise got captured. The friends then planned to help the tortoise. The hunter was just about to carry the tortoise on his back when he noticed the crow fly towards him. This made the hunter drop the tortoise. Then the deer came out and made the hunter chase him. The mouse came and nibbled the net for the tortoise to escape. When the hunter came back after a fail chase to the deer, he saw all the animals were gone.

Moral: True friends always help each other.

16. THE FARMER AND THE THREE CHEATS

Three cheats decided to trick a farmer. The first cheat walked up to the farmer and asked, "Sir, why are you carrying a dog?" "This is not a dog. It is a goat," the farmer replied. Then came the second cheat, who went up to the farmer and asked, "Sir, why are you carrying a dead calf?" "This is not a dead calf, this is a goat," the farmer answered back angrily. Then came the third cheat. He went up to the farmer and asked, "Sir, why are you carrying a donkey?" On hearing his question, the farmer was now confused. "I am carrying a goat, not a donkey," he replied in a shaky voice. The farmer thought, "Am I carrying some devil animal?" He threw the goat on the ground and fled. The three cheats laughed at the farmer's foolishness and took the goat for themselves.

Moral: Do not listen to people who are trying to trick you.

17. THE CLEVER HARE

In a jungle, a lion demanded an animal as prey every day. One day, it was the hare's turn to be the lion's prey. On reaching the place, the hare pretended to breathe heavily. "What happened? Your home is nearby, you didn't have to run," the lion said. "Sir, I just escaped another lion on the way. He called himself the King of the jungle and wanted to eat me. So I ran and came to you," the hare said. "What? Another lion? And he dares call himself the King," the lion said in anger. "Take me to him!" the lion ordered. So the hare brought the lion to a well. "He's down there." the hare said, pointing inside the well. The lion peeped and saw his reflection. But the foolish lion thought it was another lion. In anger, he jumped inside the water to attack but ended up drowning. The cunning hare saved all the animals from the cruel lion.

Moral: Intelligence is superior to physical strength.

18. THE SHEPHERD BOY AND THE WOLF

A shepherd boy loved joking with his villagers. One day, he shouted, "Wolf! Help!" Hearing his cries, the villagers thought he was in trouble. But on reaching they saw there was no wolf. The villagers got angry and left. The next day, the shepherd did the same. The villagers shouted back at him and left in anger. One day, when the shepherd was lying under the tree while his sheep grazed the grass, a wolf came and attacked his sheep. Seeing this, the shepherd was now scared and shouted in fear, "Wolf! Help!" The villagers said among themselves, "Oh that shepherd, We won't fall for his trick again." So no one went to help the shepherd, and the wolf attacked the shepherd.

Moral: We must not lie, as one day it can make us fall into trouble.

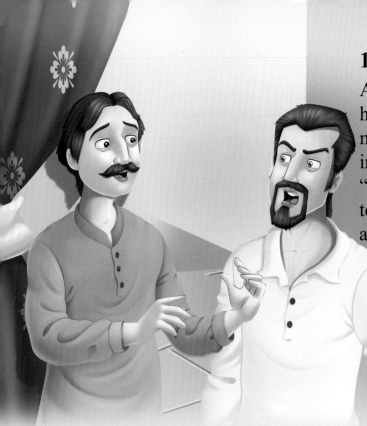

19. TIT FOR TAT

A merchant once left his precious iron rod with his friend and went out to work. When the merchant returned, he asked his friend for the iron rod he had left him. The friends answered, "I am sorry, my friend, but a mouse came and took it away." Hearing this, the merchant was angry but thought of punishing his friend. So he came the next day and said to his friend, "I have bought some gifts for you. Send your son to pick them up." When the son came, the merchant captured him. The man went to the merchant and asked for his son. "I am sorry, but the bird came and took him away." Both the friends then started to fight. Hearing the fight, the town mayor came. He asked what had happened and at once understood the truth. He ordered both of them to return the belongings to each other.

Moral: We must be truthful and honest.

20. THE TRUTHFUL DEER

A hunter once attacked a deer drinking water by a river. Surprised to see the arrow, the deer requested the hunter saying, "Sir, please don't kill me yet. Let me meet my family once before I die." The hunter did not believe the deer, so he followed the deer to his home. On reaching, he saw the deer meeting his wife and children. When the deer told them about the hunter, the deer family turned towards the hunter saying, "We are a family who cannot live without each other. Please kill us too." Seeing their love and bond as a family, the hunter lets them go free. "Your family love has taught me a great lesson. I will never kill any animal again," said the hunter. Suddenly, they heard a voice from heaven that said the deer and the hunter had found a place in heaven.

Moral: Pure-hearted will always find a place in heaven.

21. THE BLUE-DYED JACKAL

A curious jackal once fell into a barrel full of blue dye. Oh no, I'm entirely blue," he cried. As he walked into the jungle returning to his home, the animals thought he was a strange new animal. The jackal had an idea. "Let me fool these animals by telling them I am from heaven and have come to rule over them. In this way, I will command all the animals to bring me whatever I want," he thought to himself. All the animals started obeying the jackal. Suddenly at a distance, a group of jackals began to shout at the top of their voice. Hearing their voices, the blue-dyed jackal couldn't help but yell back in response. At once the animals knew who this strange animal was and started to beat him up, turning him naturally blue.

Moral: Do not lie about who you are.

22. GREED IS A CURSE

In a river, a fisherman once caught a golden fish that could grant wishes. Wow! Hold on, let me ask my wife and get back to you. You stay here," he said and ran to tell his wife. "Of course, ask her to make me a queen and give me a big palace to stay," the fisherman's wife said. "Are you sure you want to ask that?" the fisherman asked in doubt. "Yes! Now hurry up," his wife said. So the fisherman ran back and asked for what his wife wanted. At once his wish was fulfilled. In place of his cottage was a big palace and his wife was dressed like a queen. But she did not remember her husband. "Guards, throw this man out of my palace," she commanded. Saddened to see what had happened, the man went back to the Queen Fish. "Please give my old wife and my old cottage back," he cried. Poof! His wish was fulfilled.

Moral: Greed is undoubtedly a curse.

23. THE LION AND THE FOOLISH DONKEY

A proud lion commanded his servant jackal to fetch food for him. The jackal caught a donkey and asked him, Hello, my friend. I would like to invite you to a party my friend lion has thrown in your honour." the jackal said. The foolish donkey believed the words of the jackal and went with him. On seeing the donkey, the lion did not wait and pounced on him immediately. But the donkey somehow escaped. "Mighty lion, you should have waited for the donkey to get near you. You have scared it away," the jackal said. "I don't care; go get him back," the lion commanded. The jackal went back and found the donkey. He somehow convinced the donkey. And the foolish donkey again went with the jackal. This time the lion caught him and went to take bath. When he came back, he saw the donkey's brain was missing. He turned to the jackal in anger, "Did you steal the brain of the donkey?" "No sir, if he had a brain, he would not have come again," the sly jackal responded, laughing to himself as he had stolen the donkey's brain.

Moral: If you have a brain, use it wisely.

24. AN ANT AND A GRASSHOPPER

An ant carrying a piece of cheese told his musician friend grasshopper to collect food for winters on time. "But the winter is still a long way off," the grasshopper said as he laughed at the hard-working ant. Soon it was winter. The grasshopper was now shivering and cold and very hungry. He went to the ant to ask for some food he had stored. "Sorry, my friend, but there is only enough food for my family. It might be difficult for me to share it with you," the ant responded sadly. The grasshopper understood, if only he had not been lazy in summer, he would be doing well in the winter.

Moral: We must not be lazy and prepare ourselves for the future when we have time.

25. THE WIND AND THE SUN

Once, the Wind challenged the Sun to prove he is mightier. "Fine, I challenge you. Look! A man is walking down in his coat. Whoever can get him to remove his coat will prove his might." the wind said proudly. So the wind went first and started to blow air with full force. But instead of removing his coat, the man held on to his coat more tightly!

At last, the wind stopped. Now it was the sun's turn. The sun simply came out of the clouds and showered his bright warm rays over the man. Feeling the heat, the man removed his coat as it was too warm. Seeing this, the wind was in shock. "Well, I told you. Instead of force, I used gentleness. And it worked!" the sun said.

Moral: Gentleness is better than using force on someone.

26. THE HYPOCRITICAL CAT

A hare mistakenly made a bird's home, who was away, as his own house. After some days the bird came back and saw the hare had occupied his house. "Excuse me, but this is my house," the bird said. "Well, you left it for too long. Now I have settled here, and this is my house," the hare said. The two argued for a very long time. Hearing their argument, the animals of the forest suggested, they should look for a judge who will help decide their case. They found a saint-type cat sitting under a tree. The hare and the bird explained their situation to the cat one by one. "I can't understand a word you are saying. Why don't you come closer and speak near my ear," the cat said with his one eye open. The two came closer to the cat. But as they came close, the cat caught them in his big paws and made them his dinner for the night.

Moral: Bad people always take advantage of when other people quarrel.

27. THE WICKED SNAKE

An evil snake living on a tree broke the eggs of a crow couple. A fox that saw the crows crying asked, "Why are you crying?" They told him about the snake. "Don't worry. I have an idea to chase the snake away. He won't trouble you after this." the fox said confidently. Nearby, a princess was bathing. The fox saw her and asked the crows to steal the princess's necklace and drop it inside the snake's bill. The female crow did the same. Seeing the crow steal the necklace, the guards ran behind it. The crow then dropped the necklace in the snake's bill. The guards started to poke their sticks inside the bill to remove the necklace. With all the poking, the snake came out angrily and was beaten by the guards, who took the necklace away. The snake ran away from there in fear, leaving the crow family happy and peaceful. They thanked the fox for all his help.

Moral: If you are cruel to others, one day you will be punished.

28. THE TALE OF THE TWO CATS

A thin cat once asked a fat cat, "Where do you get so much food?" "I go to the palace every night and hide under the King's table. This way, I can eat a lot of food, without anyone noticing me," the fat cat explained. "Wow! Will you take me too? I would love to taste the palace food," the thin cat requested. So the fat cat agreed and took him. Just that day, the King had ordered his guards to catch any cat that tries to steal the palace's food. Before entering the palace, another cat came rushing towards the two cats and told them about the King's order. "We should leave. It's not nice to be caught by guards," the fat cat warned. But the thin cat was too determined to eat the palace food and went ahead. In doing so, he was caught by the King's guard and thrown in the little prison for animals!

Moral: We must stay happy with what we already have.

29. THE FAITHFUL MOTI

A faithful dog named Moti was barking at a thief one day. Hearing the bark, the thief got away. But his master spanked Moti after finding no one there. The next day, the thief came back. This time Moti quietly followed the thief, who took all the jewellery and hid it in a pit behind the house. The next morning, the old man saw his treasure chest empty. Disappointed, he started to wail loudly. But Moti pulled his master's shirt and brought him to the spot where the jewellery was hidden. "I am sorry, my loyal friend. I did not believe you before. Yet you saved me. Thank you!" the man said while patting Moti's head lightly.

Moral: We must treasure faithful friends and people.

30. THE HEAVENLY ELEPHANT

One night, Gopal the hermit had a dream, where an old man appeared and said, Gopal, I am gifting you this purse. If you do good deeds, your purse will be full of riches and money," the old man said. Gopal woke up and saw the purse under his pillow! The next morning, Gopal saw a beggar and his master Shyam coming from ahead. Gopal gave one rupee to the beggar, and Shyam praised him highly. But when he looked inside the purse, it was empty. At night, Gopal dreamt of the old man again. "Why are you so sad? You helped the beggar because you saw Shyam coming your way. You have already received your reward," the old man said. Gopal understood what the old man was trying to say. From the next day, Gopal did many good deeds like helping a blind lady cross the road, or offer his money to an old beggar, etc. But his purse remained empty. As Gopal was wondering about it, a heavenly white elephant came down. "Gopal, you have been a kind man. I am here to take you to heaven," the white elephant said, and he took Gopal to heaven while riding on the elephant's back.

Moral: Selfless acts of kindness will take you to heaven.

31. GRATEFUL ANIMALS, AND UNGRATEFUL MAN

Hearing strange noises, a man named Ramu peeped into a well and saw that there was a man, a tiger, and a monkey stuck inside. The man from the well shouted, "Can you help us get out?" The tiger and the monkey also pleaded. Ramu was a clever man. He asked the three inside the well, "If I help you all out, what will I get in return?" The man said, "I will do as you say." The tiger said, "I will help you in time of need." The monkey said, "I will come to you when you call me." When they all came out, only the tiger and the monkey thanked Ramu for saving them, but the man did not. Instead, he said to Ramu, "I could have come out myself, but I was only testing if you would help or not." He refused to thank Ramu for helping him.

Moral: We should never be ungrateful to anyone, especially those who help us in need.

32. THE LIONESS AND THE YOUNG JACKAL

A lion brought a baby jackal for his wife. She asked the lion, "Where did you get this baby jackal from?" The lion said, "I found it stuck in bushes and took him out from there." The lioness said, "But its mother and father would be looking out for it. You should have left it there." "No. If I had left it there, some other animal would have come and hurt this baby. So, I thought it would be better and safer for this baby jackal to be here with us" said the lion. The lioness then began to look after the young jackal. The lioness had children of her own too. They all started playing with each other and lived as a family.

Moral: No matter who is in need, you must help them.

33. THE BIRDS AND THE MONKEYS

One day, when baby birds began to come out of the eggs, some monkey heard them chirping loudly. At first, he didn't understand why they were making so much noise. So, he began to rock the nest so that the babies would quieten down. The monkey said to the babies in the nest, "Don't worry, I will rock you till your mother comes." But as soon as the monkey began rocking the nest, some of the eggs fell off the nest. Just then, the mother bird came and caught the falling eggs. She put back the eggs in the nest and said to the monkey, "Please don't shake the nest; otherwise, all the eggs will fall off the nest." But the monkey wouldn't listen and kept shaking the nest. The mother bird got angry and pricked the monkey in the face. The monkey ran away and never came back again.

Moral: You should not trouble others nor do any harm to them.

34. ELEPHANTS AND THE KING OF MICE

Some mice suddenly one day challenged the Elephant King and asked for his throne. The king elephant said to the mice, "That's not possible. I am the King and this throne belongs to me." The mice replied, "Prove yourself to be stronger and this throne will be yours." The Elephant King agreed. The next day, all the elephants and mice gathered near a pond. The chief of mice said, "If you can dig small holes as we did, then you win." The elephants said, "And if you can lift this big log, then you win." Indeed, the elephants won as the mice were not as strong as the elephants.

Moral: Never think yourself to be better than others.

35. A PROUD, LEARNED PERSON

An educated man started talking to three fishermen he met one day. The fishermen knew how proud this learned man was of himself. So, they wanted to test him. The first fisherman said, "I will ask you a riddle. If you can answer, then we will agree that you are the most learned person." The man agreed. The second fisherman asked him the riddle, "What has hands but doesn't clap?" The man was puzzled. He kept thinking and said, "I'm sorry. I don't know the answer to this riddle." The third fisherman said, "It is a clock. It has hands, but it cannot clap." The fishermen told this learned man that he should not think others less of him.

Moral: Pride goes before fall. Never think of others less of yourself.

36. PENALTY FOR PLEASING EVERYONE

A father and a son, who was sitting on a donkey, were going to the market. On their way, a girl who saw them said, "How bad is this boy!. The son got down and asked his father to sit on the donkey. A little further, they met a man who said to the father, "You are making your son walk while you are sitting on the donkey so comfortably." The father got down and started to walk beside his son. Soon they met another man who said to them, "You both are making the donkey walk so much. It must be so tiring." Both of them without giving another thought tied the donkey upside down to a long bamboo and carried him. On the way, whosoever saw them broke into laughter. The laughter frightened the donkey. It kicked hard and got its feet loose. Soon it was free and galloped away.

Moral: You cannot please everyone. Do what is right.

37. THE FOX AND TURTLE

A fox caught a turtle from a river to eat him. The turtle cried, "Please! Don't eat me. If you promise to leave me, I'll give you something wonderful to eat." Although the fox is clever, he agreed because he was greedy too. The fox left the turtle back into the water, waiting for something better to eat. As soon as the turtle went into the water, the fox cried, "You promised to give me something better to eat. Where are you going now?" The turtle said, "You can go and find something for yourself. I'm going to live here with my family." The fox was angry at himself for trusting the turtle.

Moral: Be kind to others. Don't harm anyone.

38. THE WICKED HERON

One day, an evil heron caught a bluefish. The bluefish was very angry at the heron. The fish said to heron, "Leave me at once, or else I will turn you into a tree, and you will never be able to eat us again." The heron did not believe the fish and still wanted to eat it. The fish said again, "You know, you have a lovely voice. Why don't you sing so that more fish will come near and you can eat all of them too?" The heron agreed. As soon as the wicked heron opened its mouth to sing, the fish from his mouth jumped out and swam far away."

Moral: If you are kind to others, you will be a happy person.

39. THE BIRD WITH TWO HEADS

Once, there lived a bird with two heads on a huge tree. One day, one of the heads saw a delicious fruit and picked it up. As he began to eat the fruit, the other head said, "Please, let me also taste it." But the first head laughed and said, "You will have the benefit of it when it reaches our stomach." The second head got angry and began to fly here and there. The fruit fell down. Finally, they both decided that whatever they find, they will share with each other.

Moral: Always share with others. Don't be selfish.

40. THE HORSE AND THE LION

A farmer demanded an old horse to bring a lion if he wants to live with him. On his way, the horse found a sly fox and confided his sorrow. "Don't worry, my friend. I have an idea. Just lie still in the middle of the road, and the lion's skin will be yours," the fox said. Unsure, the horse lay still in the middle of the road.

Meanwhile, the clever fox tempted the lion to a ready-made meal. "Tie your tail to the horses', directed the fox. Foolishly, the lion did that. But as soon as the lion tied their tails, the fox shouted, "Run horse, run!" The horse galloped to the farm with his prize. He was happy to be back with the kind farmer and sniff in the warm hay.

Moral - The mind is mightier than the body.

41. THE LION AND THE WOODCUTTER

Once, a lion lived in a thick forest, with two good friends, a crow, and a jackal, who fed on the remains of its' prey. As a woodcutter was chopping wood one day, he heard a sound. Swinging around, he saw a lion ready to spring upon him. The woodcutter addressed the lion as the King of the forest, and invited it to a meal cooked by his wife! He said that if the lion ate those vegetables, it would stop eating flesh!

The hungry lion relished the tasty vegetables. The woodcutter invited the lion to eat with him daily, but not tell anyone. Now, the crow and jackal often went hungry and complained to the lion. One day, the woodcutter saw the lion coming with the crow and jackal. The woodcutter thought that if its' friends could make it break a promise, they could make it kill him also. So he left the lion. The lion repented at having lost a good friend.

Moral: Don't break a promise made to a friend.

42. THE WISER DIFFER

A teacher once told an officer, "If you put your money in the right place, it increases." The officer met a poor man and gave him some money. He told him to keep it safe as it will help him to become rich soon. The poor man took the money and kept it under his hat. An eagle came and flew away with it. The poor man cried that he would not be able to become rich now. Then the teacher gave some money to the poor man and said, "You should use it to do some small business." At last, the officer and the poor man understood.

Moral: When you use your talents wisely, they increase more.

43. HOW A FOOL BECAME WISE

One day, the father told his foolish son to go and cut some branches from the tree and bring them. The son agreed. He took the chopper and went into the forest to cut some branches. He quickly climbed the tree and sat on the branch which he began cutting. Just then, a wise man was passing by. He called the boy and said, "What are you doing? You are sitting on the same branch which you are cutting. You will surely fall." The boy quickly got down and came to the man and said, "Surely, you are very wise. Please teach me how to be wise." The man began to teach him and gave him some good lessons. The boy listened carefully and promised to be wiser in the future.

Moral: It is never too late to learn good and right things from others.

44. THE SCULPTOR'S BLUNDER

In a competition, a sculptor began making statues of the same kind. He wanted to make ten of the same type. When he finished making nine statues, he thought to himself, "I will not make ten statues, but instead I will stand with the statues. Nobody will be able to recognise me." When the judge came around to see the sculptor's work, he said, "These are only nine statues. Where is the tenth one?" The sculptor quickly shouted, "Sir, I am the tenth one!" The judge disqualified the sculptor for trying to cheat.

Moral: Never try to cheat anyone and always be honest.

45. THE KING GOES TO WAR

During a war, the Lion King's ministers brought a complaint. They said to the King, "Your Majesty! It is of no use to take the donkey and the rabbit. They are of no use to us." But the king lion replied, "No, no! The donkey will blow the trumpet for us and the rabbit, which can run fast, will bring news quickly to us. All the animals are useful to me. We should work as a team."

Moral: When you work as a team, you can never be alone or weak.

46. THE WAR OF CROWS AND OWLS

On a silent night, owls and crows noisily got into a big fight. The owl cried, "Hoo-Hoo." The crows shouted, "Caw! Caw!" The owls said to the crows, "We cannot sleep during the day because you all make so much noise." The crows replied, "You all also make so much noise at night that we are not able to sleep." Then, a wise old owl said to them, "Why not make separate nests in separate trees? This way, no one will disturb the other."

Moral: Instead of fighting, look for a solution and live peacefully with others.

47. THE CROW AND THE SWAN

Once, a crow asked a swan, "How come you are so white, and I'm so black?" The swan replied, "That's because I am always in water and keep clean." The crow said that he too wanted to become like the swan. So, he began to swim in the water. As soon as he went into the water, he began to drown. He was not able to swim. The crow quickly flew out of the water and sat on a tree branch. The swan, who was wiser than the crow, said to him, "You should be happy with who you are. You should not try to become someone else."

Moral: Be happy with the way you are made. Everyone is unique.

48. WHOM TO TRUST?

On a farm, a crow asked all animals, "How can you tell whom we can trust?" The horse replied, "I think I would only trust my master." The donkey replied, "I don't need to trust anyone. I am smart enough." Suddenly, it began to rain heavily. The horse's master quickly took the horse inside. The shepherd took the goat inside, and the cow also was taken to safety. But the donkey kept sitting in the rain and did not move. He thought he is not like others and wanted to prove that he was the smartest. But soon, he started to feel cold and fell sick. Finally, he too had to look for a safe place.

Moral: Trust those who care for you.

49. THE REWARD OF SACRIFICE

Shivering in cold and hunger, a man prayed to God, "God, please take care of me." A family of pigeons sitting on the branch of the tree heard his prayers. They felt sad for the man and decided to help him. First, they threw their empty nest to the man so that he could warm himself. The man used the nest to make a fire. Then the pigeons dropped down the fruits of the trees and sacrificed their eggs to give food to the man. The man took the fruit and eggs and ate them to his heart's content. Seeing this, God was pleased with the sacrifice of the pigeons. "You have saved that man. In return, I will reward you with healthy children," God said to the pigeons. The pigeons were very happy, as they had new eggs in place of the eggs they had given to the man.

Moral: Sacrifice is always rewarded.

50. GOLD GROWS IN THE FARM

A woman once told her lazy husband that growing chickpeas would bring gold. When the time came, he saw only the chickpeas plants coming out but no gold. He went to his wife and said to her, "You said that gold would come out but it's only chickpeas." The wife then said, "This time I'll give you wheat to grow. Then for sure, gold will grow." The man agreed and went and sowed wheat in his field. When the time came, there was a golden harvest of wheat everywhere. The man went to his wife and said, "You again fooled me. There is no gold but only the wheat." The wife wanted to teach her husband a lesson since he was a lazy man. She said to him, "The wheat that you see is the gold. See the colour. It's so beautiful. Don't they look like gold?"

Moral: You should not be lazy. Work hard, and you will be rewarded.

51. THE TWO BAGS

Once, a wise man was gifted two bags. One bag had his neighbours' faults. The other bag had his flaws, which he was told to carry in front. He had to say to others about his faults. By mistake, the man put his bag on his back! He would look into the wrong bag, and tell every one of his neighbours' faults. In doing so, he faced a lot of problems. He went to the wise man again and told him about his mistakes. The man corrected his mistakes. From that day on, he lived a happy life.

Moral: We should always accept our mistakes and work upon them.

52. THE GREEDY TRAVELLER AND THE HUNGRY TIGER

A poor man had a sad encounter with a tiger. "Don't be afraid! Come near and see what I have," the tiger said. When the man went near the tiger, he saw a gold bangle. He wished to get the gold bangle. He thought, "I will sell the gold bangle and look after my family." The tiger said to the man, "I can give you this gold bangle only if you promise to feed me." But as soon as he took the bangle, the man ran away. When he reached his village and showed it to the goldsmith, the goldsmith said, "Where did you get this fake gold bangle? It is of no use." The man was sorry for what he had done.

Moral: Greed can bring a lot of trouble for us.

53. A WISE MAN

A rich man sat outside an inn he built, searching for a caretaker. Finally, he offered the job to the stranger! The rich man said, "I kept a broken stone in one of the steps to test people." All those who stepped on it, either hurt themselves or fell. But nobody thought of removing it." The stranger quickly threw away the stone and evened the ground again. The stranger was happy to accept the job. He took good care of the inn.

Moral: A person who thinks of others and does for them without being told is good and wise.

54. A CUNNING FRIEND

Once upon a time, there was a jackal named Chandu, who had a friend Girdhar, the camel. Chandu suddenly wanted to sing aloud while eating sugarcanes. Girdhar told him, "Don't do so, or the farmers of this field would come and beat me because I have not finished eating yet!" But Chandu didn't stop shouting. The farmer heard him and came. He began beating Girdhar, just as he had thought. When Girdhar ran to the bank of the river, Chandu pretended that he was feeling sorry for him. Girdhar decided to teach him a lesson. When they were going back, he said, "I want to lie down in the water!" Chandu got scared, but Girdhar lay down in the river, and Chandu drowned.

Moral: As you sow, so shall you reap.

55. THE HEN THAT LAID SILVER EGGS

A greedy woman once found a hen who laid silver eggs. She decided, "the hen must eat more so that it can lay more eggs." One day, the hen was not eating. So the woman forced the hen to eat a lot of food. The next morning, she hoped that the hen would have laid more than one egg. But she was shocked to find that her hen had fallen sick. It stopped giving any more silver eggs.

Moral: Don't be greedy. Always be happy with what and how much you have.

56. THE SPARROWS AND THE ELEPHANT

A wild elephant once broke the eggs of some sparrows. This made the sparrows very sad, so they made a plan with their friends, the frog, the crows, and the flies. The next morning, when the elephant went to the lake, the flies began buzzing around his ears. The elephant quickly closed his eyes. Just then, the crows started hitting his eyes. He was not able to open his eyes to see where he was going. The frog jumped near a deep ditch and croaked loudly. He thought that he was near the lake and the elephant walked towards the lake. He fell inside the deep hole!

Moral: You should always be kind to each other.

57. THE TACTICS OF VICTORY

A princess wanted to marry the man who would defeat her in a race. On hearing this, a farmer's son decided to participate. He placed ten gold bricks at an equal distance in the path. The race started, and the princess ran fast, leaving him far behind. A little later, she couldn't believe her eyes when she saw a gold brick! She bent to pick it up and raced on. Then, she saw another gold brick, and another, and another. She kept stopping for the gold bricks. The farmer's son left the princess behind when she picked the ninth brick. She still stopped to pick up the tenth! At last, the princess married the farmer's son!

Moral: An intelligent mind can be better than physical strenght.

58. RIGHT-MIND AND WRONG-MIND

Long ago, Wrong-Mind asked his friend, Right-Mind, to go with him to another city to earn some money. They both kept some money with them and buried the rest under a tree. After some days, Wrong-Mind accused the Right-Mind, "You stole all my money!" Right-Mind was shocked. They went to court. The judge said to them, "Go and ask the spirit of the tree." Wrong-Mind took his father's help. His father hid inside the bark of the tree as told by him. He was also told to say to the judge that Right-Mind was a thief. When they reached the tree, they thought there was something wrong. Right-Mind set fire to the tree! Wrong-Mind's father came out of the hiding! The surprised judge now knew the truth. He punished Wrong-Mind.

MORAL: Never cheat on anyone.

59. AN HONEST WOODCUTTER

A poor woodcutter once dropped his axe in a river. An angel quickly went into the water and came out with a gold and silver axe. When the angel asked the woodcutter which one was his, he said, "No, these are not mine." Then the angel brought him the axe which belonged to him. The poor man thanked the angel. The angel was so proud of his honesty that he gave him the gold and silver axes. The woodcutter became rich. When his friend, who was a greedy man, came to know about this, he did the same thing. The angel of water came up again. The greedy man said that the gold axe was his. The angel did not come back, and the greedy man lost his iron axe too.

Moral: Honesty is the best policy.

60. STOLEN FRUITS ARE NOT ALWAYS SWEET!

Once a farmer upon reaching his farm saw four people eating his tomatoes in the field without his permission. He got furious but realised that he was alone. So he said, "I welcome you all!" He told one man that he should sit in a special place and took him to a lonely corner to beat him up. He threw him out of his farm! He did the same with others too. The four people were very sad about what had happened. An old saint came to them. He said, "Since you did not take the farmer's permission, he did the right thing." They all realised that they had done wrong.

Moral: Bad deeds bring bad results.

61. THE GOLDEN BIRD AND THE KING

A hunter once caught a golden bird, but in fear from the King, brought it to the palace. He said to the King, "Your majesty, this bird can lay golden eggs." The King was happy. His servants said to the King, "Your majesty. The hunter has made a fool of you!" So, the King told his servants to free the bird in the woods! The bird thought that this kingdom was full of fools; the hunter knew it could lay golden eggs, but gifted him to the King! The King listened to his servants and asked them to set it free!

Moral: Make a decision only after you know the truth.

62. THE GREEDY LITTLE BIRD

One day, a greedy bird went to the queen bird and told her about some bullock carts. She said, "It is unsafe to go there, as any bird might get hit by the wheels." The queen bird told the others not to go there. The greedy bird always went alone. One day, it got hit by the wheels of the cart and lay injured. When he did not return, the other birds looked for him and found him poorly hurt on the village road. The queen said the bird had suffered because of its' greed.

Moral: A greedy and selfish person always suffers.

63. AN ELEPHANT AND A TAILOR

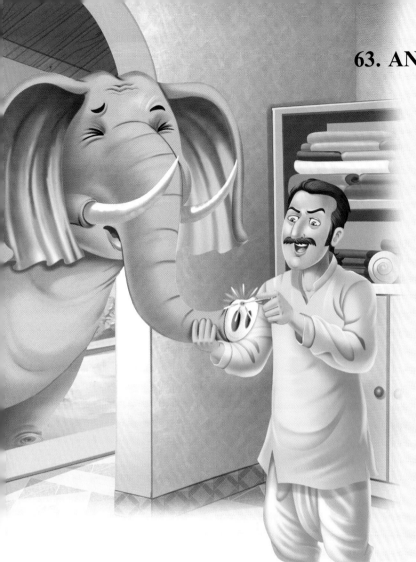

A kind tailor always fed an elephant near his house. One day, the tailor was fighting with his customer. When the elephant came, the tailor pricked the elephant's trunk with his needle out of anger. The elephant was hurt and quickly went away. The elephant thought to himself, "I will teach the tailor a lesson!" He went and stored a lot of muddy water from the river and sprayed it on the tailer in anger. It also sprinkled on some of the new dresses the tailor had made! The tailor was angry, but after some time, he realised his lousy behaviour. He went to the elephant and apologised.

Moral: Never misbehave with a friend.

64. THE MILKMAID

A young milkmaid told her daughter, "You can buy whatever you like from the money you will get after selling the milk." Her daughter was delighted. She thought of buying a hen at first. Then, she would exchange the hen's chicks for a bull, which she would sell to buy a small house. When the girl was walking on the road while thinking about all these things. She did not see a stone on the way. She fell over it and the milk spilt on the ground which broke all her dreams.

Moral: Never daydream. Work hard to fulfil all your dreams.

65. THE HARE AND THE TORTOISE

A hare once challenged a tortoise to a race. After some distance, when the hare could not see the tortoise, he decided to rest.

Meanwhile, the tortoise kept on going slowly. When the hare woke up, he ran towards the finish point. Upon reaching the finishing point, he saw that the tortoise had already arrived there. He was surprised and thought, "How is this possible?" Even being slow, the tortoise did not give up and steadily reached the finish point. All the animals were cheering for the tortoise!

Moral: Slow and steady wins the race.

66. THE MONKEYS AND THE CAP SELLER

One day, some monkeys playfully took all the caps of a cap seller who was sleeping under a tree. When he woke up, he saw that his bag was empty! He looked up and saw the monkeys laughing and them wearing his caps. He shouted at them, "Give my caps back!" They began to do just as the cap seller was doing. The cap seller was worried. He thought of a solution to get out of this problem. The cap seller threw down his cap. The monkeys did the same. He quickly collected all his caps and left happily.

Moral: Quick thinking can solve the problem.

67. UNITED WE STAND

In a jungle, a wise elephant told all the animals to stay together from being attacked by the lion. Everybody thought a lot about it and they all finally agreed. They planned and went into the jungle as one herd. The animals would all shout together whenever they heard or saw the lion. Now the lion was scared and got confused. He was not able to attack even one animal. The lion realised that he could no longer do anything to any of them, and became their friend.

Moral: United we stand, divided we fall.

68. A FRIENDLY ADVICE

Once there was a lazy farmer who did not look after his field. A friend once told the lazy farmer, "If you see a white swan, you will have a good life." Early the next morning, the farmer went to the river. He couldn't see the swan. He saw a man stealing his wheat, and one of the servants stealing milk. Because of the magical white swan, the farmer woke up early. There was no more theft. He began working hard and became healthy. When his friend came again, the farmer said, "I have not seen the white swan." The friend said, "The white swan was 'honest work', while goodness and happiness are for those who work hard."

Moral: Fortune favours those who work hard.

69. THE FATE OF A FOOL

Three thieves saw a fool carrying a goat. As the fool came closer, the first thief took his goat away quietly. The fool found that his goat was missing. The second thief asked him, "Why are you so sad?" The fool said that he had lost his goat. The thief said, "The wind has taken your goat, and if you give me your horse, I could bring back your goat." The fool agreed. After waiting for a long, he realised that he had lost his horse too! The third thief came to him and said he could take him to his horse and goat, and took him to a nearby well. The fool removed his clothes and jumped in. Finding nothing inside, he came out to find that his clothes were also gone!

Moral: Never be foolish and use your wisdom.

70. THE DISHONEST MILKMAN

A dishonest milkman always sold milk mixed with water. The day came when his son was going to get married. He quickly collected the money from those who used to buy milk from him. He bought a lot of jewellery and dresses. He was returning home by boat. When he reached the middle of the stream, the boat overturned. Everything that he had bought fell into the river and floated away. He cried, "Please help! Somebody!" He heard a voice telling him how he used to add the river's water to the milk. He realised his mistake and promised never again to do wrong.

Moral: Everyone suffers from their misdeeds one day.

71. THE GAME OF WIT

A family of jackals found an empty lion's den to live. The father jackal hid inside, while his wife protected the den. When the lion came back, the mother jackal shouted. At this, the father jackal asked his cubs to shout aloud. The surprised lion stopped right there. He heard the father jackal saying, "The children are crying for the lion's meat." The lion got scared. The fox told him about what the jackals had planned. They both came to the den. When they saw them, the mother jackal scolded the fox. She said, "Why did you return with one lion when I had asked you for five?" Both the lion and fox ran away.

Moral: The physically weak can defeat the strong with a sharp mind and cleverness.

72. THE CLEVER JACKAL

In a jungle, all the animals made a plan to save themselves from being eaten by a lion. The jackal was the most intelligent animal among them. The jackal told the elephant, "When the lion comes to eat you, you just lie down and don't move. The lion will think that you are already dead." When the lion came, the elephant pretended he was dead and lay on the ground without moving. The lion asked the jackal, who was standing there, "What happened to the elephant?" The jackal said, "Dear Lion, the elephant ate something from some tree and fell very ill. Now, if you will eat it, you will fall sick, and you will never be able to eat again." The lion got worried and promised never to return to that jungle.

Moral: Wisdom leads to victory.

73. THE CROW AND THE QUAIL

Once, a crow and a quail spotted a man carrying a pot of curd. The crow dipped its beak into the pot. The curd was fresh and sweet. So, the crow kept drinking the curd from the pot. This made the pot shake. The cowherd set it on the ground and looked around. At once, the crow flew away. The quail was flying slowly. As it came closer to the pot, the cowherd thought that it was the quail that had finished all the curd. He hit the poor quail with a stone which made the crow laugh. He did not help the quail and flew away.

Moral: Better to be alone than in bad company.

74. THE LION AND THE CAMEL

Once there lived a lion with his three friends – a crow, a jackal, and a leopard. One day, a camel lost his way and met the lion. The camel asked, "Can I please stay here?" The lion welcomed his guest and let him stay with them. One day the lion fell very sick. He was unable to go on hunts. The lion's friends suggested the lion, "We should ask the camel to bring us food." But the lion did not agree and said, "He does not belong to our forest. He may get lost deep in the forest." The camel heard him and said, "You have been kind to me. I will go and look for food." All the animals praised the camel and the crow decided to help him. And, they both went in search of food.

Moral: Always have the spirit of working together and be thankful to others for helping you.

75. THE SNAKE AND FOOLISH FROGS

There lived an old snake near a pond. Because of old age, the snake had become very weak. In the pond, lived many frogs. One day, the prince of frogs when saw the old snake thought of helping him. He took the snake to his parents. The king and queen frogs took good care of the old snake. In just a few days, he was strong and swift again. And he started eating the frogs. At last one day came when only the three frogs remained. The wicked snake hunted them too.

Moral: Stay away from the bad.

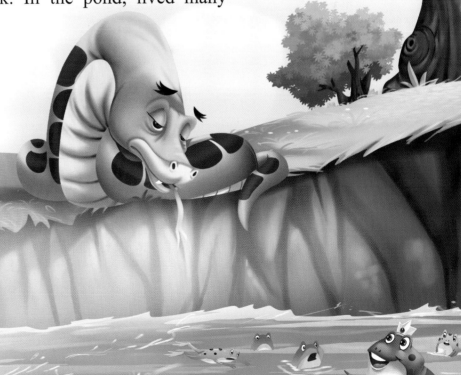

76. THE DISCONTENTED DOG

One warm summer day, Sheru, the dog thought to himself, "If I could just stay in this freshwater all day long, that would be great." But a goldfish told a surprised Sheru, "While you wish that, I wish I could roll on the soft, warm grass like you!" Seeing a sparrow, Sheru wished he could fly. But the sparrow said to Sheru, "I wish I could play all day long like you and did not have to build a nest or search hard for food!" The unhappy rooster said it had to wake up his master each dawn. Even the sheep was unhappy. Sheru thought to himself, "Nobody is happy with what they have!" And so he decided to enjoy being himself.

Moral: Appreciate what you have and be yourself.

77. THE STUBBORN HUNTER

One evening, a hunter caught a rabbit. He told his friend, "I am going to make this my dinner!" Just as he raised his knife, the rabbit slipped from his hold and the knife landed on his foot. The hunter groaned in pain, his foot bled, and the rabbit escaped. His friend cleaned and bandaged the hunter's wound and said, "This was justice from heaven!" From that day, the hunter stopped hunting animals for good.

Moral: Bad deeds soon receive their punishment.

78. THE FISHERMAN AND THE FISH

One day, a fisherman cast his net into a pool. He was lucky to catch a fish. It was a tiny fish, and the fisherman was very happy. The little fish tried to fool the fisherman by begging to be set free. She said, "Please let me go. I am too tiny. If you catch me now, I will be of no use to you. But if you catch me when I grow big, I will be of use to you then." The fisherman thought for some time. He remarked, "Don't try to fool me! If I let you go now, I will never see you again. So, I won't let you go."

Moral: Don't let anyone fool you. Always take decisions after you think well about the situation.

79. THE TALKATIVE TORTOISE

One summer some swans decided to stay in a faraway lake. They knew they could quickly fly. But a tortoise knew he would be unable to travel such a long distance. The swans made a smart plan, as they did not wish to leave their friend behind. They each held one end of a stick in their beaks, while the tortoise held the centre with his teeth. But, the swans warned him, "Do not speak, or you would crash to the ground!" But the talkative tortoise did not listen. As he opened his mouth to speak, he lost his grip on the stick and fell to the ground.

Moral: We must learn to wait and be patient.

80. THE UGLY TREE

In a dense forest, all tall trees would make fun of a bent tree, calling it ugly. The bent tree wondered why God had not made it like the other trees, as birds never made their nests on it, nor could it give shade to travellers. One day, a woodcutter came to cut down some trees. Seeing the twisted tree, he thought he would not be able to cut long, straight logs from it. As he went near the beautiful trees with his axe, the trees got scared. One by one, he cut down all the straight trees, who thought of themselves better than the bent tree. The twisted tree thanked God for not making it the way it was.

Moral: We must learn to be content with what God has given us.

81. THE JEALOUS SOLE

A group of fish got together and decided, "We should select a king, to maintain peace and order among us." He further added, "A race should be held, and the fastest fish would be selected as the king." Everyone thought about it for some time. After finding no other way, the fishes agreed and took part in the race. They found that the herring had come first. But the sole felt very jealous and twisted its mouth. Since then, the sole's mouth has remained twisted on one side. This was considered as its punishment.

Moral: We should never be jealous of anyone.

82. THE GREEDY MOUSE

A mouse found a corn basket and squeezed himself inside it. He ate all the corn to his heart's content, but could not come out, as his belly had grown bigger! A rabbit passed by and heard the mouse crying. The rabbit went to the mouse and told him to wait till his belly became smaller. The mouse fell asleep. On waking up, his belly had become smaller, but he ate more corn. Again, his belly grew bigger, and he slept. After a while, a cat came. She smelled the mouse and offered help. But instead, she caught him and took him away.

Moral: Greed can cause a lot of trouble.

83. TWO ROOSTERS AT QUARREL

Two roosters were fighting to rule the farmyard. One of them became the winner and said, "I am the master of this farmyard." Feeling proud of himself, he crowed and flapped his wings with all his might. Just at the moment an eagle flying overhead swooped down, caught up the crowing rooster. The rooster screamed, but no one could help him. The eagle flew away with the winning rooster. The farmyard now belonged to the defeated rooster.

Moral: Pride goes before destruction.

84. THE LION AND THE BEAR

A bear and a lion were arguing over a deer. "It is mine," the lion argued. "No! It is mine," the bear said back. Neither wanted to share their catch. At this, a fight broke out between them. Soon, they were tired and lay down. There was a fox who had been watching. He dodged them and took the deer. He ran away from there. The lion and the bear were shocked. They thought that if they had shared their prey in a friendly way, they both could have had a good meal. But now they had nothing, while the fox was eating a good meal!

Moral: Sharing shows how much we care.

85. THE FLY AND THE ANT

A fly and an ant were arguing about who is better. The fly said, "You are a tiny creature. Whenever sweets were prepared, I am the first to taste them, and even sit on the heads of kings!" The ant replied, "Though I am tiny, I am wise. I save my food during summer so that I would not go hungry during winter." While they were arguing, a man came there with a flyswatter. He saw the fly and chased it away. The ant laughed and mocked at the proud fly.

Moral: We should never be too proud and continue the path of hard work.

86. THE ANT AND THE PIGEON

A pigeon named Raja once saved an ant from drowning using a leaf. The ant was grateful and told the pigeon, "I am so thankful to you for saving my life. If ever you need

anything, let me know!" They became the best of friends. Some days later, the pigeon was resting. Along came a hunter, and aimed an arrow at it. The ant climbed up the hunter's leg and bit him hard. The hunter screamed and missed his aim, and the pigeon flew away to safety.

Moral: Even a single good deed can get great rewards.

87. THE KING AND THE FOOLISH MONKEY

A king asked his pet monkey who sat beside him, "Could you please fan me as I am feeling very hot?" Suddenly, a fly came and sat on the King's chest. The monkey drove the fly away with the fan, but the fly kept coming back, again and again. It sat on the King's face, and then on his nose. Irritated and angry, the monkey wanted to kill the fly. So, when it next sat on the King's nose, the monkey hit it with a sword. The fly flew away, but the sword fell on the King's nose leaving him severely wounded.

Moral: It is better to have a wise friend than a foolish one who can cause trouble for you.

88. THE OAK TREE AND THE REEDS

Once, a giant oak tree was boasting about itself to the reeds, "I can stand upright in a storm, while you, the weak reeds, could be easily bent by the slightest breeze." The reeds replied, "The winds did not harm us. We bow before the wind, and so do not break." One night, a hurricane swept over the place. It tore out the oak tree from its roots. But, the reeds stood in their place, bowing low.

Moral: You should be down to earth because pride makes you fall.

89. THE GOLDEN GOOSE

A fairy once gave a woman a goose that laid golden eggs. The woman thought, "The goose must have a huge lump of gold within its body. I must get it all at once!" She decided to get all the gold at one time. So, she killed the goose, but found there was no gold inside! She started crying and realised her fault that she had lost even the single golden egg she used to get each day.

Moral: Being selfish and greedy can lead you to ruin.

90. THE WOLF IN SHEEP'S CLOTHING

A cunning wolf once thought to himself, "If I wear the sheep's skin and find a flock of sheep, I will no longer be hungry." He put it over his own body and looked like a sheep. He started to find a big flock of sheep to fool them with his dress-up. Finally, he found a flock of sheep and quietly joined them. But the alert shepherd knew something was different. He thought, "Let me carefully see him. This is not a sheep. It's a wolf!" He decided to teach him a lesson. He tied a rope to the wolf's tail and hung him from the branch of a tree!

Moral: Beware of enemies who think they may fool you.

91. THE FOX WITHOUT A TAIL

On a bright sunny day, a fox sadly caught in a trap! After a long struggle, he was free, but his tail stayed in the trap! He wondered, "What would I do without my fluffy tail, and how would I face the other foxes?" He called a meeting of all the foxes. They were shocked to see him and asked what had happened to his tail. The fox said, "I have cut off my tail, as it is more fashionable and comfortable." An old fox sensed the truth. "You are saying this, as you are embarrassed to be without a tail," she said. "If you hadn't lost your tail, you wouldn't have asked us to cut off our tails!" All the other foxes laughed aloud and went away.

Moral: Wrong tricks don't work.

92. THE WOLF AND THE GOAT

Early in a summer morning, a wolf spotted a goat and shouted, "Miss Goat! Why are you taking such danger for your life by grazing on a steep rock? Eat from down here." The goat thought for a while. But, she sensed the wolf's plan, and replied, "I know you are not thinking of me, my friend, but rather yourself! I know if I come down, you will make a good meal out of me. So, I prefer to stay here out of your reach." The goat saved herself from the wolf by not going down. The wolf learned a lesson from the wise goat and never returned to that place.

Moral: Always be careful in what you do, or else you will regret it.

93. THE MISER

Once there was a miser. He had a lump of gold which he never liked to spend. So he dug up a hole near the tree in his garden and buried it there. Each day, he would go to keep a check on it. One of his servants noticed this. So, he went quietly and dug up the hole, and found the gold. The next day, when the miser went to gaze at his treasure, he found nothing but an empty hole! He began to cry loudly. Listening to his cries, his friend came running there and asked, "Have you ever spent any of your gold!"

"No!" replied the miser. "Looking at it made me happy!" At this, his friend picked up a stone and threw it into the hole, and said, "Cover up this stone and look into the hole and think the gold is still inside it." He started to laugh and left.

Moral: Better use what you already have, or else you will regret it if you lose it.

94. THE GREEDY DOG

Once a very greedy dog found a juicy bone to eat. He held it tightly in his mouth and strolled towards a lonely place. On the way, the dog had to cross a bridge built over a small stream. While crossing the bridge, he saw his reflection in the water. Seeing it, he thought that there was another dog with a bone, in the water. "How nice it would be to take that bone away from the other dog!" the greedy dog thought to himself. In wondering so, the dog started barking. The moment he opened his mouth, the bone fell into the water. Thus, the greedy dog did not get any bone and lost his bone too. He felt pathetic and realised his mistakes.

Moral: Greed brings a feeling of regret.

95. THE MONKEY'S JUSTICE

Two cats found two pieces of bread. One of the pieces was slightly bigger than the other. The first cat claimed it for itself, "This is mine since I had seen the loaf first." But, the second cat said, "That doesn't matter. It is mine!" A fight broke in between them. At that moment, a monkey was passing by. Cunningly, he asked them, "Why are you fighting?" Learning of the reason, he said, "I could make the pieces equal." He took a bite from the bigger piece, but the other piece became bigger! He continued doing this until nothing was left and ran away. The cats realised they should have shared the loaf as it was, for now, they had no bread left at all!

Moral: If two people are fighting, the third one takes an undue advantage.

96. GREED LEADS TO SUFFERING

A hunter spotted a big, fat donkey in a forest. He shot an arrow at it, injuring it severely. But, the donkey injured the hunter before dying. A greedy fox, who had been hiding behind a bush, saw all this. It thought, "Indeed, this is my lucky day! Today, I will feed on a donkey and a man!" The fox went to the donkey first. But when the fox started to eat the donkey, the sharp tip of the hunter's arrow that had injured the donkey, hurt the throat of the fox. As a result, the fox was injured too and ran away.

Moral: We should never be greedy as it gives nothing in return.

97. THE SNAKE AND THE ANTS

There was once a poisonous snake who lived in a hole. He thought, "I am the most powerful of all. Everybody is scared of me. I am the King of the jungle." One day, he saw an anthill near the hole in which he lived. He was outraged. He decided to destroy the ugly anthill and attacked it. As he was about to attack the anthill, one of the ants saw him. He quickly went inside and warned everybody. Within moments, thousands of ants came out and bit the snake all over his body. The snake couldn't bear the pain and ran away from there.

Moral: Pride can cause you to fall hard.

98. THE CROW AND THE HUNTER

A flock of crows lived on a banyan tree. A witty crow also lived in the same tree. One day, the witty crow saw a hunter coming to that tree. He spread many grains on the ground, planning to cast his net when the crows ate the grains. The crow flew to warn the other crows of the danger in their path. He said, "There is a hunter who has spread grains on the ground to catch you all! Do not go there." But the crows ignored his warning and started feeding on the grains. Just as they had begun to eat, a net fell around them. The hunter's trick worked, and the crows were caught.

Moral: Never ignore advice that can be useful.

99. THE ROOSTER AND THE JEWEL

A long time ago, a rooster was scratching the ground. Suddenly he found a diamond. At first, he was pleased to see the shining diamond. He wondered how he must go about it. But when he hit it, he found it was too hard. He couldn't eat it. Looking at the jewel, he thought, "This gem may be very costly, but to me, it is a single grain of corn which is more useful than all the world's jewels." He kept it on the ground and again began searching for his food.

Moral: No matter how expensive a gem might be, it cannot take the place of food.

100. THE BEAR AND THE BEES

A bear was searching for food when he spotted a honeycomb. The bear was attracted to it, so he went closer. When the bear sniffed at it, a bee stung him sharply. It hurt the bear a lot and made him angry. He thought, "I will not forgive the bees and will destroy their honeycomb!" He went back to the honeycomb and gave them a warning. The bees said, "We are not scared of you. It was you who troubled us!" The bear became angrier, and he destroyed the honeycomb with his paws. At this, the entire swarm became angry and stung the bear all over his body! The poor bear ran away to save himself.

Moral: We should not trouble anyone for our comfort.

101. THE HUNTER AND THE RABBIT

A hunter once captured a rabbit. The rabbit was scared at first, but then calmed itself down. It was a brilliant rabbit. He thought of a plan to save himself. He said to the hunter, "I will show you a place full of gold to keep you rich for the rest of your life if you let me go." The hunter got very greedy after listening to the deal. He said, "Where is the place? You will have to show it to me now!" The clever rabbit replied, "You first have to leave me, then you can follow me." The moment the hunter placed the rabbit on the ground, the rabbit ran away. The hunter watched the rabbit flee in deep regret, but he could do nothing now.

Moral: Being patient will help you in every situation.